The Open University

M208 Pure Mathematics

AA1

Numbers

This publication forms part of an Open University course. Details of this and other Open University courses can be obtained from the Student Registration and Enquiry Service, The Open University, PO Box 197, Milton Keynes, MK7 6BJ, United Kingdom: tel. +44 (0)870 333 4340, e-mail general-enquiries@open.ac.uk

Alternatively, you may visit the Open University website at http://www.open.ac.uk where you can learn more about the wide range of courses and packs offered at all levels by The Open University.

To purchase a selection of Open University course materials, visit the webshop at www.ouw.co.uk, or contact Open University Worldwide, Michael Young Building, Walton Hall, Milton Keynes, MK7 6AA, United Kingdom, for a brochure: tel. +44 (0)1908 858785, fax +44 (0)1908 858787, e-mail ouwenq@open.ac.uk

The Open University, Walton Hall, Milton Keynes, MK7 6AA.

First published 2006.

Edited, designed and typeset by The Open University, using the Open University TEX System.

Printed and bound in the United Kingdom by Hobbs the Printers Limited, Brunel Road, Totton, Hampshire SO40 3WX.

ISBN 0 7492 0207 6

1.1

Contents

Introduction to Analysis Block A

The analysis units of this course are concerned with the study of functions whose domains and codomains are subsets of the real line $\mathbb{R}$. In Analysis Block A we begin to study such functions from a precise point of view in order to prove many of their properties. Some of these properties may seem intuitively obvious, but this work will provide a sound basis for the study of more difficult properties of functions later in the course.

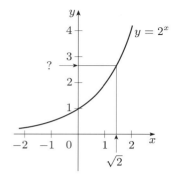

For example, consider the problem:

Does the graph $y = 2^x$ have a gap at $x = \sqrt{2}$?

Later in the block we answer this question by showing that the function $f(x) = 2^x$ has a property called *continuity*, so its graph has no gaps. Before we can tackle this problem, however, we must answer the question:

What precisely is meant by $2^{\sqrt{2}}$?

Thus, to answer a question about functions, we first need to clarify our ideas about real numbers.

Introduction

This unit is devoted to the real numbers and their properties. In particular, we discuss inequalities, which play a crucial role in analysis.

In Section 1 we start by revising rational numbers and their decimal representations. Then we introduce the real numbers as infinite decimals, and describe their properties and the difficulties involved in doing arithmetic with such decimals.

Some of the properties of real numbers discussed in this section were introduced in Unit I3, Section 1.

In Section 2 we discuss the rules for manipulating inequalities, and show how to find the solution set of an inequality involving a real variable x by applying these rules. We also explain how to deal with inequalities which involve modulus signs.

In Section 3 we describe various techniques for proving inequalities; this section includes an audio devoted to the proofs of several inequalities which are needed in later analysis units.

The concept of a *least upper bound*, which is of great importance in analysis, is introduced in Section 4, where we also discuss the Least Upper Bound Property of $\mathbb{R}$.

In Section 5 we describe how least upper bounds can be used to define arithmetic operations in $\mathbb{R}$.

Study guide

You will already be familiar with much of the early material in this unit and so you should spend most of your study time on Sections 2, 3 and 4 in order to gain facility with manipulating inequalities.

The sections should be studied in the natural order. Section 5 is intended for reading only and will not be assessed directly.

The video is a general one which can be watched at any time during your study of the unit. It starts from an elementary level, and explains how the real number system is composed of the rationals and the irrationals.

The video touches on many of the key ideas in the unit, including:
1. rational numbers, whose decimals terminate or recur;
2. ordering the real numbers;
3. a geometric proof of the fact that $\sqrt{2}$ is irrational;
4. the reason why $(-1) \times (-1) = +1$;
5. the fact that $0.999\ldots = 1$;
6. arithmetic with real numbers, using truncations of their decimals and the Least Upper Bound Property.

1   Real numbers

After working through this section, you should be able to:

(a) explain the relationship between *rational numbers* and *recurring decimals*;

(b) explain the term *irrational number* and describe how such a number can be represented on a number line;

(c) find a rational and an irrational number between any two distinct real numbers.

In this section we discuss the real numbers and describe some of their properties. We start with the rationals and investigate their decimal representations, and then proceed to the irrational numbers.

1.1   Rational numbers

The set of **natural numbers** is

$$\mathbb{N} = \{1, 2, 3, \ldots\},$$

the set of **integers** is

$$\mathbb{Z} = \{\ldots, -2, -1, 0, 1, 2, \ldots\}$$

and the set of **rational numbers** is

$$\mathbb{Q} = \{p/q : p \in \mathbb{Z}, q \in \mathbb{N}\}.$$

Note that 0 is not a natural number.

Remember that each rational number has many different representations as a ratio of integers; for example,

$$\frac{1}{3} = \frac{2}{6} = \frac{10}{30} = \cdots.$$

Rational numbers satisfy the usual arithmetical operations of addition, subtraction, multiplication and division of rational numbers. They can be represented on a number line.

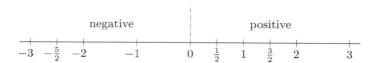

For example, the rational $\frac{3}{2}$ is placed at the point which is one half of the way from 0 to 3.

This representation means that rationals have a natural *order* on the number line. For example, 19/22 lies to the left of 7/8 because

$$\frac{19}{22} = \frac{76}{88} \quad \text{and} \quad \frac{7}{8} = \frac{77}{88}.$$

If a lies to the left of b on the number line, then we say that

a is *less than* b or b is *greater than* a

and we write

$a < b$ or $b > a$.

For example, we write

$$\frac{19}{22} < \frac{7}{8} \quad \text{or} \quad \frac{7}{8} > \frac{19}{22}.$$

Also, we write $a \leq b$ (or $b \geq a$) if either $a < b$ or $a = b$.

Exercise 1.1   Arrange the following rationals in order:

$$0, \quad 1, \quad -1, \quad \frac{17}{20}, \quad -\frac{17}{20}, \quad \frac{45}{53}, \quad -\frac{45}{53}.$$

Exercise 1.2   Show that between any two distinct rationals there is another rational.

1.2 Decimal representation of rational numbers

The decimal system enables us to represent all the natural numbers using only the ten integers

$$0, 1, 2, 3, 4, 5, 6, 7, 8, 9,$$

which are called *digits*. We now remind you of the basic facts about the representation of *rational* numbers by decimals.

Definition   A **decimal** is an expression of the form

$$\pm\, a_0.a_1 a_2 a_3 \ldots,$$

where a_0 is a non-negative integer and a_n is a digit for each $n \in \mathbb{N}$.

For example,
$$0.8500\ldots,$$
$$13.1212\ldots,$$
$$-1.111\ldots,$$
are all decimals.

If only a finite number of the digits $a_1, a_2, \ldots$ are non-zero, then the decimal is a **terminating** or **finite decimal**, and we usually omit the tail of zeros.

For example,
$$0.8500\ldots = 0.85.$$

Terminating decimals are used to represent rational numbers in the following way:

$$\pm\, a_0.a_1 a_2 \ldots a_n = \pm\left(a_0 + \frac{a_1}{10^1} + \frac{a_2}{10^2} + \cdots + \frac{a_n}{10^n}\right).$$

It can be shown that any fraction whose denominator contains only powers of 2 and/or 5 (for example, $20 = 2^2 \times 5$) can be represented by such a terminating decimal, which can be found by long division.

For example,
$$0.85 = 0 + \frac{8}{10^1} + \frac{5}{10^2}$$
$$= \frac{85}{100} = \frac{17}{20}.$$

However, if we apply long division to other rationals, then the process of long division never terminates and we obtain a **non-terminating** or **infinite decimal**. For example, applying long division to $1/3$ gives $0.333\ldots$ and for $19/22$ we obtain $0.86363\ldots$.

Exercise 1.3   Find the decimal corresponding to $1/7$.

The infinite decimals which are obtained by applying the long division process have a certain common property. All of them are **recurring decimals**; that is, they have a repeating block of digits, so they can be written in shorthand form as follows:

$$\begin{aligned} 0.333\ldots &\quad = 0.\overline{3}, \\ 0.142\,857\,142\,857\ldots &\quad = 0.\overline{142\,857}, \\ 0.863\,63\ldots &\quad = 0.8\overline{63}. \end{aligned}$$

Another commonly used notation is
$$0.\dot{3} \quad \text{and} \quad 0.\dot{1}42\,85\dot{7}.$$

Whenever we apply the long division process to a fraction p/q, the resulting decimal is recurring. To see why, note that there are only q possible remainders at each stage of the division, so one of these remainders must eventually repeat. When this happens, the block of digits obtained after the first occurrence of this remainder will be repeated infinitely often. If the remainder 0 occurs, then the resulting decimal is finite; that is, it ends in recurring 0s.

Infinite recurring decimals which arise from the long division of fractions are used to represent the corresponding rational numbers. This representation is not quite so straightforward as for finite decimals, however. For example, the statement

$$\frac{1}{3} = 0.\overline{3} = \frac{3}{10^1} + \frac{3}{10^2} + \frac{3}{10^3} + \cdots$$

can be made precise only when we have introduced the idea of the sum of a convergent infinite series. For the moment, when we write the statement $1/3 = 0.\overline{3}$ we mean simply that the decimal $0.\overline{3}$ arises from $1/3$ by the long division process.

This idea is discussed in Unit AA3.

The following example illustrates one way of finding the rational with a given decimal representation.

Example 1.1   Express in the form of a fraction the rational number whose decimal representation is $0.8\overline{63}$.

Solution   First we find the fraction x such that

$$x = 0.\overline{63}.$$

If we multiply both sides by 10^2 (because the recurring block has length two), then we obtain

$$100x = 63.\overline{63} = 63 + x.$$

Hence

$$99x = 63, \quad \text{so} \quad x = \frac{63}{99} = \frac{7}{11}.$$

Thus

$$0.8\overline{63} = \frac{8}{10} + \frac{x}{10} = \frac{8}{10} + \frac{7}{110} = \frac{95}{110} = \frac{19}{22}. \quad \blacksquare$$

The key idea in the above solution is that multiplication of a decimal by 10^k moves the decimal point k places to the right.

> **Exercise 1.4**   Using the above method, find the fractions whose decimal representations are:
> (a) $0.\overline{231}$;   (b) $2.2\overline{81}$.

Decimals which end in recurring 9s sometimes arise as alternative representations for terminating decimals. For example,

$$1 = 0.\overline{9} = 0.999\ldots \quad \text{and} \quad 1.35 = 1.34\overline{9} = 1.349\,99\ldots.$$

When possible, we avoid using the form of a decimal which ends in recurring 9s.

You may find this rather disconcerting, but it is important to realise that this representation is a matter of *definition*. We wish to allow the decimal $0.999\ldots$ to represent a number x, so x must be less than or equal to 1 and greater than each of the numbers

This definition is discussed in the video.

$$0.9, \ 0.99, \ 0.999, \ \ldots.$$

The *only* rational with these properties is 1.

The decimal representation of rational numbers has the advantage that it enables us to decide immediately which of two distinct positive rationals is the greater. We need examine only their decimal representations and notice the first place at which the digits differ. For example, to order 7/8 and 19/22, we can write

$$\frac{7}{8} = 0.875 \quad \text{and} \quad \frac{19}{22} = 0.863\,63\ldots.$$

Then

$$\downarrow \qquad \qquad \downarrow$$
$$0.863\,63\ldots < 0.875, \quad \text{so} \quad 19/22 < 7/8.$$

Exercise 1.5   Find the first two digits after the decimal point in the decimal representations of 17/20 and 45/53, and hence determine which of these two rationals is the greater.

1.3 Irrational numbers

You have already seen earlier in the course that there is no rational number which satisfies the equation $x^2 = 2$. A number which is not rational is called **irrational**. There are many other mathematical quantities which cannot be described exactly by rational numbers; for example, $\sqrt[m]{n}$, where m and n are natural numbers and $x^m = n$ has no integer solution, as well as the numbers π and e.

See Unit I3, Section 1.

It is natural to ask whether irrational numbers, such as $\sqrt{2}$ and π, can be represented as decimals. Using your calculator, you can check that

$$(1.414\,213\,56)^2$$

We discuss π and e in the video for Unit AA2. The video for this unit discusses $\sqrt{2}$.

is very close to 2, so $1.414\,213\,56$ is a very good approximate value for $\sqrt{2}$. But is there a decimal that represents $\sqrt{2}$ exactly? If such a decimal exists, then it cannot be recurring because all the recurring decimals correspond to rational numbers.

In fact, it is possible to represent all the irrational numbers mentioned so far by non-recurring decimals. For example, there are non-recurring decimals representing $\sqrt{2}$ and π, the first few digits of which are

$$\sqrt{2} = 1.414\,213\,56\ldots \quad \text{and} \quad \pi = 3.141\,592\,65\ldots.$$

We prove that $\sqrt{2}$ has a decimal representation in Subsection 5.2.

It is also natural to ask whether arbitrary non-recurring decimals, such as

$$0.101\,001\,000\,100\,001\ldots \quad \text{and} \quad 0.123\,456\,789\,101\,112\ldots$$

represent irrational numbers. We take it as a basic assumption about the number system that they do.

Thus the set of irrational numbers consists of all the non-recurring decimals.

1.4 Real numbers and their properties

Together, the rational numbers (recurring decimals) and irrational numbers (non-recurring decimals) form the set of **real numbers**, denoted by $\mathbb{R}$.

As with rational numbers, we can determine which of two real numbers is greater by comparing their decimals and noticing the first pair of corresponding digits which differ. For example,

$$\overset{\downarrow}{} \qquad\qquad \overset{\downarrow}{}$$
$$0.101\,001\,000\,100\,001\ldots < 0.123\,456\,789\,101\,112\ldots.$$

When comparing decimals in this way, the decimal on the left should not end in recurring 9s. As noted earlier, any decimal ending in recurring 9s has an alternative representation as a terminating decimal.

We now associate with each irrational number a point on the number line. For example, the irrational number

$$x = 0.123\,456\,789\,101\,112\ldots$$

satisfies each of the inequalities

$$0.1 < x < 0.2$$
$$0.12 < x < 0.13$$
$$0.123 < x < 0.124$$
$$\vdots$$

We assume that there is a point on the number line corresponding to x which lies to the right of each of the rational numbers 0.1, 0.12, 0.123, ... and to the left of each of the rational numbers 0.2, 0.13, 0.124, ...

As usual, negative real numbers correspond to points lying to the left of 0. The number line, complete with both rational and irrational points, is called the **real line**.

There is thus a one-one correspondence between the points on the real line and the set $\mathbb{R}$ of real numbers.

We now state several order properties of $\mathbb{R}$ with which you are probably already familiar, although you may not have met their names before.

Order properties of $\mathbb{R}$

1. **Trichotomy Property**   If $a, b \in \mathbb{R}$, then *exactly one* of the following inequalities holds:

   $$a < b \quad \text{or} \quad a = b \quad \text{or} \quad a > b.$$

2. **Transitive Property**   If $a, b, c \in \mathbb{R}$, then

   $$a < b \text{ and } b < c \implies a < c.$$

3. **Archimedean Property**   If $a \in \mathbb{R}$, then there is a positive integer n such that

   $$n > a.$$

4. **Density Property**   If $a, b \in \mathbb{R}$ and $a < b$, then there is a rational number x and an irrational number y such that

   $$a < x < b \quad \text{and} \quad a < y < b.$$

These properties are used frequently in analysis and we do not always refer to them explicitly by name.

The use of the symbol $\Rightarrow$ to represent 'implies' is discussed in Unit I2, Section 3.

The first three of these properties are almost self-evident, but the Density Property is not so obvious. One consequence of the Density Property is that between any two distinct real numbers there are infinitely many rational numbers and infinitely many irrational numbers. Rather than prove the Density Property, we give an example which illustrates how it can be proved for general numbers a and b.

Example 1.2   Let $a = 0.12\overline{3}$ and $b = 0.123\,45\ldots$. Find a rational number x and an irrational number y such that

$$a < x < b \quad \text{and} \quad a < y < b.$$

Solution   The two decimals

$$a = 0.123\overset{\downarrow}{3}3\ldots \quad \text{and} \quad b = 0.123\,\overset{\downarrow}{4}5\ldots$$

differ first at the fourth digit. If we truncate b after this digit, then we obtain the rational number

$$x = 0.1234,$$

which satisfies $a < x < b$.

To find an irrational number y between a and b, we attach to x a (sufficiently small) non-recurring tail such as $010\,010\,001\ldots$ to give

$$y = 0.1234\,|010010001\ldots.$$
$$\text{non-recurring tail}$$

Thus $a < y < b$ and y is irrational, since its decimal is non-recurring.   ■

Exercise 1.6

(a) Let $a = 0.\overline{3}$ and $b = 0.3401$. Find a rational number x and an irrational number y such that $a < x < b$ and $a < y < b$.

(b) Given positive real numbers a and b such that $a < b$, describe how you can find a rational number x and an irrational number y such that $a < x < b$ and $a < y < b$.

1.5 Arithmetic with real numbers

We can do arithmetic with recurring decimals by first converting the decimals to fractions. However, it is not obvious how to do arithmetic with non-recurring decimals. For example, assuming that we can represent $\sqrt{2}$ and π by the non-recurring decimals

$$\sqrt{2} = 1.414\,213\,56\ldots \quad \text{and} \quad \pi = 3.141\,592\,65\ldots,$$

can we also represent the sum $\sqrt{2} + \pi$ and the product $\sqrt{2} \times \pi$ as decimals? What is meant by the operations of addition and multiplication when non-recurring decimals (irrationals) are involved, and do these operations satisfy the usual properties of addition and multiplication stated in the following table?

These properties were discussed in Unit I3, Section 1.

Arithmetic in $\mathbb{R}$

Addition	Multiplication	
A1. If $a, b \in \mathbb{R}$, then $a + b \in \mathbb{R}$.	M1. If $a, b \in \mathbb{R}$, then $a \times b \in \mathbb{R}$.	CLOSURE
A2. If $a \in \mathbb{R}$, then $a + 0 = 0 + a = a$.	M2. If $a \in \mathbb{R}$, then $a \times 1 = 1 \times a = a$.	IDENTITY
A3. If $a \in \mathbb{R}$, then there is a number $-a \in \mathbb{R}$ such that $a + (-a) = (-a) + a = 0$.	M3. If $a \in \mathbb{R} - \{0\}$, then there is a number $a^{-1} \in \mathbb{R}$ such that $a \times a^{-1} = a^{-1} \times a = 1$.	INVERSES
A4. If $a, b, c \in \mathbb{R}$, then $(a + b) + c = a + (b + c)$.	M4. If $a, b, c \in \mathbb{R}$, then $(a \times b) \times c = a \times (b \times c)$.	ASSOCIATIVITY
A5. If $a, b \in \mathbb{R}$, then $a + b = b + a$.	M5. If $a, b \in \mathbb{R}$, then $a \times b = b \times a$.	COMMUTATIVITY
D. If $a, b, c \in \mathbb{R}$, then $a \times (b + c) = a \times b + a \times c$.		DISTRIBUTIVITY

We can summarise the contents of this table as follows:

- $\mathbb{R}$ is an Abelian group under the operation of addition $+$;
- $\mathbb{R} - \{0\}$ is an Abelian group under the operation of multiplication $\times$;

and these two group structures are linked by the distributive property. Any system satisfying the properties listed in the table is called a **field**.

Groups are defined in Unit GTA1, Section 3.

Certainly the set $\mathbb{Q}$ of rationals forms a field, but it is not clear that the set $\mathbb{R}$ of real numbers does. As mentioned above, we have not yet defined addition and multiplication of real numbers. However, these definitions can be made, and it can be proved that all the above properties hold in $\mathbb{R}$. Since this is a lengthy process, we *assume* from now on that it has been carried out. Furthermore, we assume that the set $\mathbb{R}$ contains the nth roots and rational powers of positive real numbers, with their usual properties.

In Section 5 we describe one way to justify these assumptions, and also remind you of the properties of powers.

Remark   Analysis texts take various approaches to defining real numbers. For example, it is common to assume that there exists a set $\mathbb{R}$ which is a field containing $\mathbb{Q}$ and having certain extra properties, and then to deduce all results from these assumptions. In this 'axiomatic approach' the definition of the real numbers themselves may not be given (though they can be defined by a somewhat abstract procedure involving subsets of $\mathbb{Q}$ called 'Dedekind cuts'), but it is proved that each real number must have a decimal representation. We have chosen a more concrete approach in which real numbers are *defined* to be decimals.

Further exercises

Exercise 1.7   Arrange the following numbers in increasing order:

(a) 7/36, 3/20, 1/6, 7/45, 11/60;

(b) $0.\overline{465}$, $0.4\overline{65}$, $0.46\overline{5}$, 0.4655, 0.4656.

Exercise 1.8   Find the fractions whose decimal representations are:

(a) $0.\overline{481}$;   (b) $0.48\overline{1}$.

Exercise 1.9   Let $x = 0.\overline{21}$ and $y = 0.\overline{2}$. Find $x + y$ and xy in decimal form.

Exercise 1.10   Find a rational number x and an irrational number y in the interval $(0.119, 0.12)$.

2   Inequalities

After working through this section, you should be able to:

(a) solve inequalities by rearranging them into simpler equivalent forms;

(b) solve inequalities involving modulus signs.

2.1 Rearranging inequalities

Much of analysis is concerned with inequalities of various kinds; the aim of this section and the next is to provide practice in their manipulation.

The fundamental rule, on which much manipulation of inequalities is based, is that the statement $a < b$ means exactly the same as the statement $b - a > 0$.

Rule 1 $a < b \Leftrightarrow b - a > 0$.

The use of the symbol $\Leftrightarrow$ to represent 'if and only if' is discussed in Unit I2, Section 3.

Put another way, the inequalities $a < b$ and $b - a > 0$ are equivalent.

There are several other standard rules for rearranging a given inequality into an equivalent form. Each of these can be deduced from Rule 1. For example, we obtain an equivalent inequality by adding the same expression to both sides.

Rule 2 $a < b \Leftrightarrow a + c < b + c$.

Another way to rearrange an inequality is to multiply both sides by a *non-zero* expression, making sure to reverse the inequality if the expression is negative.

Rule 3   If $c > 0$, then
$$a < b \Leftrightarrow ac < bc;$$
if $c < 0$, then
$$a < b \Leftrightarrow ac > bc.$$

For example,
$$2 < 3 \Leftrightarrow -2 > -3.$$

Sometimes the most effective way to rearrange an inequality is to take reciprocals. However, both sides of the inequality must be positive and the direction of the inequality has to be reversed.

Rule 4   If $a, b > 0$, then
$$a < b \Leftrightarrow \frac{1}{a} > \frac{1}{b}.$$

For example,
$$2 < 3 \Leftrightarrow \tfrac{1}{2} > \tfrac{1}{3}.$$

Some inequalities can be simplified only by taking powers. In order to do this, both sides must be non-negative and the power must be positive.

> **Rule 5**   If $a, b \geq 0$ and $p > 0$, then
>
> $\qquad a < b \ \Leftrightarrow\ a^p < b^p.$

For positive integers p, Rule 5 follows from the identity

$$b^p - a^p = (b - a)(b^{p-1} + b^{p-2}a + \cdots + ba^{p-2} + a^{p-1});$$

For example,

$$b^3 - a^3 = (b - a)(b^2 + ba + a^2).$$

since the value of the right-hand bracket is positive, we deduce that

$$b - a > 0 \ \Leftrightarrow\ b^p - a^p > 0.$$

For other positive real numbers p the proof of Rule 5 is harder, but the rule remains true, as you will see later in the block.

There are corresponding versions of Rules 1–5 in which the *strict* inequality $a < b$ is replaced by the *weak* inequality $a \leq b$. For example, if $c > 0$, then

$$a \leq b \ \Leftrightarrow\ ac \leq bc.$$

Another rule for rearranging an inequality into an equivalent form is given in Subsection 2.3.

Also, we frequently use the usual rules for the sign of a product:

$\times$	$+$	$-$
$+$	$+$	$-$
$-$	$-$	$+$

In particular, the square of any real number is non-negative.

2.2 Solving inequalities

Solving an inequality involving an unknown real number x means determining those values of x for which the inequality holds; that is, finding the *solution set* of the inequality, usually given as a union of intervals. We can often do this by rewriting the inequality in an equivalent but simpler form, using Rules 1–5.

Example 2.1   Solve the inequality

$$\frac{x + 2}{x + 4} > \frac{x - 3}{2x - 1}.$$

Solution   We rearrange this inequality to give an equivalent simpler inequality, using Rule 1:

$$\frac{x + 2}{x + 4} > \frac{x - 3}{2x - 1} \ \Leftrightarrow\ \frac{x + 2}{x + 4} - \frac{x - 3}{2x - 1} > 0$$

$$\Leftrightarrow\ \frac{x^2 + 2x + 10}{(x + 4)(2x - 1)} > 0.$$

By completing the square, we obtain

$$x^2 + 2x + 10 = (x + 1)^2 + 9,$$

so the numerator is always positive. We can now find the solution set using a sign table:

Sign tables were introduced in Unit I1, Section 2. In future we shall not usually draw a sign table, but you should draw your own if you find this helpful.

x	$(-\infty, -4)$	-4	$(-4, \frac{1}{2})$	$\frac{1}{2}$	$(\frac{1}{2}, \infty)$
$x^2 + 2x + 10$	$+$	$+$	$+$	$+$	$+$
$x + 4$	$-$	0	$+$	$+$	$+$
$2x - 1$	$-$	$-$	$-$	0	$+$
$\dfrac{x^2 + 2x + 10}{(x + 4)(2x - 1)}$	$+$	$*$	$-$	$*$	$+$

So the solution set is

$$\left\{ x : \frac{x+2}{x+4} > \frac{x-3}{2x-1} \right\} = (\infty, -4) \cup \left(\tfrac{1}{2}, \infty \right). \quad \blacksquare$$

Remark   Some inequalities can be solved by cross-multiplying, using Rules 3 and 4. However, this method cannot be used in Example 2.1, since the denominators $x+4$ and $2x-1$ are negative for some values of x.

The following example illustrates some of the other rules for rearranging inequalities.

Example 2.2   Solve the inequality
$$\frac{1}{2x^2 + 2} < \frac{1}{4}.$$

Solution   Since $2x^2 + 2 > 0$, we can rearrange the inequality into an equivalent form as follows:

$$\begin{aligned}
\frac{1}{2x^2 + 2} < \frac{1}{4} &\Leftrightarrow 2x^2 + 2 > 4 \quad \text{(Rule 4)} \\
&\Leftrightarrow x^2 + 1 > 2 \quad \text{(Rule 3)} \\
&\Leftrightarrow x^2 - 1 > 0 \quad \text{(Rule 1)} \\
&\Leftrightarrow (x-1)(x+1) > 0.
\end{aligned}$$

So the solution set is

$$\left\{ x : \frac{1}{2x^2 + 2} < \frac{1}{4} \right\} = (-\infty, -1) \cup (1, \infty). \quad \blacksquare$$

Exercise 2.1   For each of the following expressions, include the expression in an inequality which is equivalent to $x > 2$.

(a) $x + 3$ (b) $2 - x$ (c) $5x + 2$ (d) $1/(5x + 2)$

Exercise 2.2   Solve the following inequalities.

(a) $\dfrac{4x - x^2 - 7}{x^2 - 1} \geq 3$ (b) $2x^2 \geq (x + 1)^2$

In the next example, we have to solve an inequality which involves rational powers. Here we need to be careful, when applying Rule 5, to ensure that both sides of the inequality are non-negative.

Example 2.3   Solve the inequality
$$\sqrt{2x + 3} > x.$$

Solution   The expression $\sqrt{2x + 3}$ is defined only when $2x + 3 \geq 0$, that is, for $x \geq -3/2$. Hence we need to consider only those x in $[-3/2, \infty)$.

Remember that $\sqrt{}$ always means the non-negative square root.

We can obtain an equivalent inequality by squaring, provided that both $\sqrt{2x + 3}$ and x are non-negative. Thus, for $x \geq 0$, we have

$$\begin{aligned}
\sqrt{2x + 3} > x &\Leftrightarrow 2x + 3 > x^2 \quad \text{(Rule 5, } p = 2) \\
&\Leftrightarrow x^2 - 2x - 3 < 0 \quad \text{(Rule 1)} \\
&\Leftrightarrow (x - 3)(x + 1) < 0.
\end{aligned}$$

So the part of the solution set in $[0, \infty)$ is $[0, 3)$.

On the other hand, if $-3/2 \leq x < 0$, then
$$\sqrt{2x + 3} \geq 0 > x,$$
so the other part of the solution set is $[-3/2, 0)$.

Here we use the Transitive Property:
$$\sqrt{2x + 3} \geq 0 \text{ and } 0 > x,$$
implies that
$$\sqrt{2x + 3} > x.$$

Hence the complete solution set is

$$\{x : \sqrt{2x+3} > x\} = [-3/2, 0) \cup [0, 3) = [-3/2, 3). \quad \blacksquare$$

Exercise 2.3 Solve the inequality

$$\sqrt{2x^2 - 2} > x.$$

2.3 Inequalities involving modulus signs

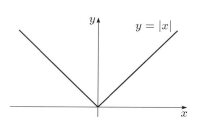

Now we consider inequalities involving the *modulus* of a real number. Recall that if $a \in \mathbb{R}$, then its **modulus**, or **absolute value**, $|a|$ is defined by

$$|a| = \begin{cases} a, & \text{if } a \geq 0, \\ -a, & \text{if } a < 0. \end{cases}$$

It is useful to think of $|a|$ as the distance along the real line from 0 to a.

For example,
$$|3| = |-3| = 3.$$

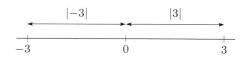

In the same way, $|a - b|$ is the distance from 0 to $a - b$, which is the same as the distance from a to b.

For example, the distance from -2 to 3 is
$$|(-2) - 3| = |-5| = 5.$$

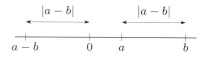

Note also that $|a + b| = |a - (-b)|$ is the distance from a to $-b$.

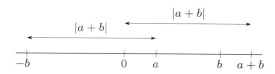

We now list some basic properties of the modulus, which follow immediately from the definition.

Properties of the modulus

If $a, b \in \mathbb{R}$, then

1. $|a| \geq 0$, with equality if and only if $a = 0$;
2. $-|a| \leq a \leq |a|$;
3. $|a|^2 = a^2$;
4. $|a - b| = |b - a|$;
5. $|ab| = |a|\,|b|$.

For example:

1. $|-2| > 0$;
2. $-|-2| \leq -2 \leq |-2|$;
3. $|-2|^2 = (-2)^2$;
4. $|-2-1| = |1 - (-2)|$;
5. $|(-2) \times 1| = |-2| \times |1|$.

There is a basic rule for rearranging inequalities involving modulus signs.

Rule 6 $|a| < b \Leftrightarrow -b < a < b.$

There is a corresponding version of this rule with weak inequalities.

It is often possible to rearrange inequalities involving modulus signs by using Rule 5 with $p = 2$. Examples 2.4 and 2.5 illustrate both approaches.

Example 2.4   Solve the inequality $|x - 2| < 1$.

Solution   We rearrange the inequality into an equivalent form:

$$|x - 2| < 1 \iff -1 < x - 2 < 1 \quad \text{(Rule 6)}$$
$$\iff 1 < x < 3.$$

Take $a = x - 2$ and $b = 1$.

So the solution set is

$$\{x : |x - 2| < 1\} = (1, 3). \quad \blacksquare$$

Example 2.5   Solve the inequality $|x - 2| \le |x + 1|$.

Solution   We rearrange the inequality into an equivalent form:

$$|x - 2| \le |x + 1| \iff (x - 2)^2 \le (x + 1)^2 \quad \text{(Rule 5, } p = 2)$$
$$\iff x^2 - 4x + 4 \le x^2 + 2x + 1$$
$$\iff 3 \le 6x$$
$$\iff \tfrac{1}{2} \le x.$$

So the solution set is

$$\{x : |x - 2| \le |x + 1|\} = \left[\tfrac{1}{2}, \infty\right). \quad \blacksquare$$

The inequalities in Examples 2.4 and 2.5 can be interpreted geometrically. The inequality

$$|x - 2| < 1$$

holds when the distance from x to 2 is strictly less than 1. So it holds when x lies in the open interval $(1, 3)$, which has midpoint 2.

Similarly, the inequality

$$|x - 2| \le |x + 1|$$

holds when the distance from x to 2 is less than or equal to the distance from x to -1, since $|x + 1| = |x - (-1)|$. Since the point halfway from -1 to 2 is $\tfrac{1}{2}$, the inequality holds when x lies in the interval $\left[\tfrac{1}{2}, \infty\right)$.

Try to use geometric intuition, where possible, to give yourself an idea of the solution set of an inequality.

Exercise 2.4   Solve the following inequalities.

(a) $|2x^2 - 13| < 5$ (b) $|x - 1| \le 2|x + 1|$

Further exercises

Exercise 2.5   Solve the following inequalities.

(a) $\dfrac{x - 1}{x^2 + 4} < \dfrac{x + 1}{x^2 - 4}$ (b) $\sqrt{4x - 3} > x$ (c) $|17 - 2x^4| \le 15$

3 Proving inequalities

After working through this section, you should be able to:

(a) state and use the Triangle Inequality;

(b) use the Binomial Theorem and mathematical induction to prove inequalities which involve an integer n.

In this section we show you how to *prove* inequalities of various types. We use the rules for rearranging inequalities given in Section 2, and also other rules which enable us to deduce 'new inequalities from old'. We met the first such rule in Section 1, where it was called the Transitive Property of $\mathbb{R}$.

Transitive Rule $a < b$ and $b < c \Rightarrow a < c$.

We use the Transitive Rule when we want to prove that $a < c$ and we know that $a < b$ and $b < c$.

For an example of this use, see Example 2.3.

The following rules are also useful.

Combination Rules   If $a < b$ and $c < d$, then

Sum Rule $a + c < b + d$;

Product Rule $ac < bd$, provided $a, c \geq 0$.

For example, if $2 < 3$ and $4 < 5$, then
$$2 + 4 < 3 + 5;$$
$$2 \times 4 < 3 \times 5.$$

There are versions of the Transitive Rule and Combination Rules involving weak inequalities, which you can work out as they arise.

Remark   The Transitive Rule and Combination Rules have a different nature from Rules 1–6 given in Section 2. Rules 1–6 tell us how to *rearrange* inequalities into equivalent forms, whereas the Transitive Rule and the Combination Rules enable us to deduce new inequalities which are not equivalent to the old ones.

3.1 Triangle Inequality

Our next inequality is also used to deduce 'new inequalities from old'. It involves the absolute values of three real numbers a, b and $a + b$, and is called the *Triangle Inequality*. As you will see, the Triangle Inequality has many applications in the analysis units.

The Triangle Inequality is related to the fact that the length of one side of a triangle is less than the sum of the lengths of the other two sides.

Triangle Inequality   If $a, b \in \mathbb{R}$, then
1. $|a + b| \leq |a| + |b|$ (usual form);
2. $|a - b| \geq \big||a| - |b|\big|$ ('backwards' form).

For example,
$$|-1 + 3| \leq |-1| + |3|;$$
$$|(-1) - 3| \geq \big||-1| - |3|\big|.$$

Proof   We rearrange the inequality into an equivalent form:

$$|a + b| \leq |a| + |b| \iff (a + b)^2 \leq (|a| + |b|)^2 \quad \text{(Rule 5, } p = 2\text{)}$$
$$\iff a^2 + 2ab + b^2 \leq a^2 + 2|a|\,|b| + b^2$$
$$\iff 2ab \leq |2ab|.$$

Remember that
$$|a|^2 = a^2.$$

This final inequality is certainly true for all $a, b \in \mathbb{R}$, so the first inequality must also be true for all $a, b \in \mathbb{R}$. Hence we have proved part 1.

We prove part 2 using the same method:

$$|a - b| \geq \big||a| - |b|\big| \iff (a - b)^2 \geq (|a| - |b|)^2$$
$$\iff a^2 - 2ab + b^2 \geq a^2 - 2|a|\,|b| + b^2$$
$$\iff -2ab \geq -|2ab|$$
$$\iff 2ab \leq |2ab|,$$

which is again true for all $a, b \in \mathbb{R}$. ■

Remarks

1. Although we have used double-headed arrows here, the proof requires only the arrows going from right to left. For example, in the proof of part 1, the important implication is

    $$|a + b| \leq |a| + |b| \impliedby 2ab \leq |2ab|.$$

2. Part 1 of the Triangle Inequality can also be proved by using Rule 6, which implies that

    $$|a + b| \leq |a| + |b| \iff -(|a| + |b|) \leq a + b \leq |a| + |b|. \tag{3.1}$$

    We know that

    $$-|a| \leq a \leq |a| \quad \text{and} \quad -|b| \leq b \leq |b|,$$

    so, by the Sum Rule,

    $$-(|a| + |b|) \leq a + b \leq |a| + |b|.$$

    Hence, by statement (3.1),

    $$|a + b| \leq |a| + |b|.$$

    A modification of this proof shows that there is a version of the Triangle Inequality with n real numbers, where $n \geq 2$:

    $$|a_1 + a_2 + \cdots + a_n| \leq |a_1| + |a_2| + \cdots + |a_n|.$$

The next example gives typical applications of the Triangle Inequality.

Example 3.1   Use the Triangle Inequality to prove that:

(a) $|a| \leq 1 \implies |3 + a^3| \leq 4$;   (b) $|b| < 1 \implies |3 - b| > 2$.

In each part, we are deducing one inequality from another, not showing that two inequalities are equivalent.

Solution

(a) Suppose that $|a| \leq 1$. The Triangle Inequality gives

$$|3 + a^3| \leq |3| + |a^3|$$
$$= 3 + |a|^3$$
$$\leq 3 + 1 \quad \text{(since } |a| \leq 1\text{)}$$
$$= 4.$$

Here we use the Transitive Rule.

Thus

$$|a| \leq 1 \implies |3 + a^3| \leq 4.$$

(b) Suppose that $|b| < 1$. The backwards form of the Triangle Inequality gives

$$|3 - b| \geq ||3| - |b||$$
$$= |3 - |b||$$
$$\geq 3 - |b|.$$

Again, we use the Transitive Rule.

Now $|b| < 1$, so $-|b| > -1$, and hence

$$3 - |b| > 3 - 1 = 2.$$

We deduce from the previous chain of inequalities that

$$|b| < 1 \implies |3 - b| > 2. \quad \blacksquare$$

Remarks

1. The results of Example 3.1 can also be stated in the form:
   (a) $|3 + a^3| \leq 4$, for $|a| \leq 1$;
   (b) $|3 - b| > 2$, for $|b| < 1$.

2. The reverse implications

   $$|3 + a^3| \leq 4 \implies |a| \leq 1 \quad \text{and} \quad |3 - b| > 2 \implies |b| < 1$$

   are false. For example, try putting $a = -\frac{3}{2}$ and $b = -2$.

   Exercise 3.1   Use the Triangle Inequality to prove that:
   (a) $|a| \leq \frac{1}{2} \implies |a + 1| \leq \frac{3}{2}$;   (b) $|b| < \frac{1}{2} \implies |b^3 - 1| > \frac{7}{8}$.

3.2 Inequalities involving integers

In analysis we often need to prove inequalities involving an integer n. It is a common convention in mathematics that the symbol n is used to denote an integer (frequently a natural number).

It is often possible to deal with inequalities involving n using the rules of rearrangement given in Section 2. Here is an example.

Example 3.2   Prove that

$$2n^2 \geq (n + 1)^2, \quad \text{for } n \geq 3.$$

Solution   Rearranging this inequality into an equivalent form, we obtain

$$2n^2 \geq (n + 1)^2 \iff 2n^2 - (n + 1)^2 \geq 0 \quad \text{(Rule 1)}$$
$$\iff n^2 - 2n - 1 \geq 0$$
$$\iff (n - 1)^2 - 2 \geq 0 \quad \text{(completing the square)}$$
$$\iff (n - 1)^2 \geq 2.$$

This final inequality is true for $n \geq 3$, so the inequality $2n^2 \geq (n + 1)^2$ is true for $n \geq 3$. $\blacksquare$

Remarks

1. In Exercise 2.2(b), we asked you to solve the inequality

   $$2x^2 \geq (x + 1)^2,$$

   and the solution set is $(-\infty, 1 - \sqrt{2}] \cup [1 + \sqrt{2}, \infty)$. In Example 3.2 we showed that all natural numbers $n \geq 3$ lie in this solution set.

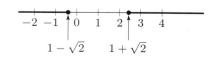

2. An alternative solution to Example 3.2 is the following:

$$2n^2 \geq (n+1)^2 \iff 2 \geq \left(\frac{n+1}{n}\right)^2 \quad \text{(Rule 3)}$$

$$\iff \sqrt{2} \geq 1 + \frac{1}{n} \quad \text{(Rule 5, } p = 2\text{)}$$

Here we use the fact that both sides of the inequality are positive.

and this final inequality certainly holds for $n \geq 3$.

Exercise 3.2 Prove that

$$\frac{3n}{n^2 + 2} < 1, \quad \text{for } n > 2.$$

3.3 Worked examples

The audio illustrates various methods for proving inequalities. Several of the inequalities that we prove will be used in later analysis units.

In addition to the techniques already described for proving inequalities, we use mathematical induction and the Binomial Theorem, restated below.

See Unit I2, Sections 3 and 4.

Theorem 3.1 Binomial Theorem

1. If $x \in \mathbb{R}$ and $n \in \mathbb{N}$, then

$$(1 + x)^n = \sum_{k=0}^{n} \binom{n}{k} x^k$$

$$= 1 + nx + \frac{n(n-1)}{2!} x^2 + \cdots + x^n.$$

2. If $a, b \in \mathbb{R}$ and $n \in \mathbb{N}$, then

$$(a + b)^n = \sum_{k=0}^{n} \binom{n}{k} a^{n-k} b^k$$

$$= a^n + na^{n-1}b + \frac{n(n-1)}{2!} a^{n-2}b^2 + \cdots + b^n.$$

The notation
$$\binom{n}{k} = \frac{n!}{k!(n-k)!}$$
is also denoted by ^nC_k.

By convention, $0! = 1$, so
$$\binom{n}{0} = \binom{n}{n} = 1.$$
Here, we also adopt the convention that
$$0^0 = 1.$$

Listen to the audio as you work through the frames.

Audio

2. $\sqrt{a^2+b^2} \le a+b$, for $a, b \ge 0$

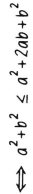

$$\sqrt{a^2+b^2} \le a+b \iff a^2+b^2 \le (a+b)^2$$
$$\iff a^2+b^2 \le a^2+2ab+b^2$$
$$\iff 0 \le 2ab.$$

Final inequality is TRUE $(a, b \ge 0)$.

Hence

$$\sqrt{a^2+b^2} \le a+b, \text{ for } a, b \ge 0.$$

Alternative version

$$\sqrt{c+d} \le \sqrt{c}+\sqrt{d}, \text{ for } c,d \ge 0.$$

> Put $a^2 = c$, $b^2 = d$ $\qquad (*)$

3. $|\sqrt{a}-\sqrt{b}| \le \sqrt{|a-b|}$, for $a, b \ge 0$

We may assume $a \ge b$; then

$\sqrt{a} \ge \sqrt{b}$ and $|a-b|=a-b$, so

$$|\sqrt{a}-\sqrt{b}| \le \sqrt{|a-b|} \iff \sqrt{a}-\sqrt{b} \le \sqrt{a-b}$$
$$\iff \sqrt{a} \le \sqrt{a-b}+\sqrt{b}.$$

> Interchanging a, b leaves inequality unchanged

Final inequality is TRUE (take $(*)$ with $c=a-b, d=b$).

Hence

$$|\sqrt{a}-\sqrt{b}| \le \sqrt{|a-b|}, \text{ for } a, b \ge 0.$$

1. $ab \le \left(\dfrac{a+b}{2}\right)^2$, for $a, b \in \mathbb{R}$

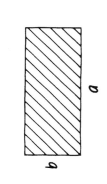

each perimeter $= 2a + 2b$

area of rectangle $\le$ area of square with same perimeter

Proof

$$ab \le \left(\frac{a+b}{2}\right)^2 \iff ab \le \frac{a^2+2ab+b^2}{4}$$
$$\iff 4ab \le a^2+2ab+b^2$$
$$\iff 0 \le a^2-2ab+b^2$$
$$\iff 0 \le (a-b)^2.$$

Final inequality is TRUE (all squares are non-negative).

Hence

$$ab \le \left(\frac{a+b}{2}\right)^2, \text{ for } a, b \in \mathbb{R}.$$

> $ab = \left(\dfrac{a+b}{2}\right)^2$ $\iff a = b$

6. $2^n \geq n^2$, for $n \geq 4$

n	1	2	3	4	5
2^n	2	4	8	16	32
n^2	1	4	9	16	25

$P(n): 2^n \geq n^2$

STEP 1: show $P(4)$ is true:
$2^4 = 16 = 4^2$, so $P(4)$ is true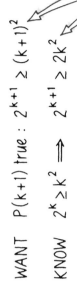

STEP 2: show $P(k)$ true $\implies P(k+1)$ true, for $k \geq 4$.

Assume $P(k)$ true: $2^k \geq k^2$, for some $k \geq 4$.

WANT $P(k+1)$ true: $2^{k+1} \geq (k+1)^2$

KNOW $2^k \geq k^2 \implies 2^{k+1} \geq 2k^2$

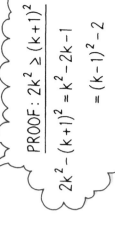
PROOF: $2k^2 \geq (k+1)^2$

$2k^2 - (k+1)^2 = k^2 - 2k - 1$
$= (k-1)^2 - 2$
≥ 0 for $k \geq 4$

So $2^{k+1} \geq (k+1)^2$.

Thus $P(k)$ true $\implies P(k+1)$ true, for $k \geq 4$. ✓

By the Principle of Mathematical Induction,
$$2^n \geq n^2, \text{ for all } n \geq 4.$$

4. $2^n \geq 1+n$, for $n \geq 1$

n	1	2	3	4
2^n	2	4	8	16
$1+n$	2	3	4	5

Binomial Theorem for $n \geq 1$:

$$(1+x)^n = 1 + nx + \frac{n(n-1)}{2!} x^2 + \cdots + x^n$$
$$\geq 1 + nx, \text{ for } x \geq 0.$$

Put $x = 1$:
$$2^n \geq 1+n, \text{ for } n \geq 1.$$

5. $2^{\frac{1}{n}} \leq 1 + \frac{1}{n}$, for $n \geq 1$

n	1	2	3	4
$2^{1/n}$	2	1.41	1.26	1.19
$1+\frac{1}{n}$	2	1.5	1.33	1.25

$$2^{\frac{1}{n}} \leq 1 + \frac{1}{n}$$
$$\iff 2 \leq \left(1 + \frac{1}{n}\right)^n$$

By the Binomial Theorem for $n \geq 1$,

$$\left(1 + \frac{1}{n}\right)^n = 1 + n\left(\frac{1}{n}\right) + \frac{n(n-1)}{2!}\left(\frac{1}{n}\right)^2 + \cdots + \left(\frac{1}{n}\right)^n$$
$$\geq 2.$$

Hence
$$2^{\frac{1}{n}} \leq 1 + \frac{1}{n}, \text{ for } n \geq 1.$$

9. An experiment

Try Bernoulli's Inequality with $x = -\dfrac{1}{2n}$:

> $-\dfrac{1}{n} < -\dfrac{1}{2n} < 0$

$$\left(1-\frac{1}{2n}\right)^n \geq 1+n\left(-\frac{1}{2n}\right) = 1-\frac{1}{2} = \frac{1}{2}$$

$$\Rightarrow \left(\frac{2n-1}{2n}\right)^n \geq \frac{1}{2}$$

$$\Rightarrow \left(\frac{2n}{2n-1}\right)^n \leq 2$$

$$\Rightarrow \frac{2n}{2n-1} \leq 2^{\frac{1}{n}}.$$

> Frame 5
> $2^{\frac{1}{n}} \leq 1+\dfrac{1}{n}$

Hence

$$1+\frac{1}{2n-1} \leq 2^{\frac{1}{n}} \leq 1+\frac{1}{n}, \quad \text{for } n = 1, 2, \ldots\ldots$$

10. Summary : possible strategies

> Try some values. Draw diagram.

- give direct proof

> Choose appropriate value of x

- use Binomial Theorem

> May need $N > 1$

- use Mathematical Induction

> e.g. Bernoulli

- deduce from known inequality

7. Bernoulli's Inequality

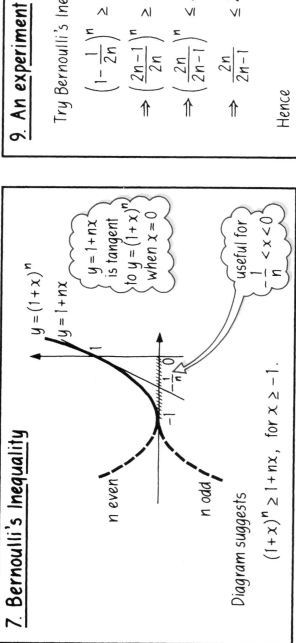

> $y = 1+nx$ is tangent to $y = (1+x)^n$ when $x = 0$

> useful for $-\dfrac{1}{n} < x < 0$

$y = (1+x)^n$

$y = 1+nx$

n even

n odd

Diagram suggests

$$(1+x)^n \geq 1+nx, \quad \text{for } x \geq -1.$$

8. Proof of Bernoulli's Inequality

$P(n): (1+x)^n \geq 1+nx$, for $x \geq -1$

STEP 1 : show $P(1)$ true :   obvious

STEP 2 : show $P(k)$ true $\Rightarrow P(k+1)$ true, for $k \geq 1$.

Assume $P(k)$ true : $(1+x)^k \geq 1+kx$, for some $k \geq 1$.   (∗)

$(1+x)^{k+1} = (1+x)^k(1+x)$ and $(1+x) \geq 0$, so by (∗),

$$\begin{aligned}
(1+x)^{k+1} &\geq (1+kx)(1+x) \\
&= 1+(k+1)x+kx^2 \\
&\geq 1+(k+1)x.
\end{aligned}$$

So $P(k)$ true $\Rightarrow P(k+1)$ true, for $k \geq 1$.

By Principle of Mathematical Induction,
$P(n)$ is true for all $n \geq 1$.

Post-audio exercises

To practise using the techniques described in the audio, we suggest that you now try the following exercises.

Exercise 3.3   Use the Binomial Theorem to prove that

$$\left(1 + \frac{1}{n}\right)^n \geq \frac{5}{2} - \frac{1}{2n}, \quad \text{for } n \geq 1.$$

Hint: Consider the first three terms in the binomial expansion.

Exercise 3.4   Prove the inequalities:

(a) $2n^3 \geq (n+1)^3$, for $n \geq 4$;   (b) $2^n \geq n^3$, for $n \geq 10$.

Exercise 3.5   Suppose that $a > 0$ and $a^2 > 2$. Prove that

$$\frac{1}{2}\left(a + \frac{2}{a}\right) < a.$$

Further exercises

Exercise 3.6   Use the Triangle Inequality to prove that

$$|a| \leq 1 \implies |a - 3| \geq 2.$$

Exercise 3.7   Prove that

$$(a^2 + b^2)(c^2 + d^2) \geq (ac + bd)^2, \quad \text{where } a, b, c, d \in \mathbb{R}.$$

Exercise 3.8   Prove the inequality

$$3^n \geq 2n^2 + 1, \quad \text{for } n = 1, 2, \ldots,$$

(a) using the Binomial Theorem, applied to $(1 + x)^n$ with $x = 2$;

(b) using mathematical induction.

Exercise 3.9   Apply Bernoulli's Inequality, first with $x = 2/n$ and then with $x = -2/(3n)$, to prove that

$$1 + \frac{2}{3n - 2} \leq 3^{1/n} \leq 1 + \frac{2}{n}, \quad \text{for } n = 1, 2, \ldots.$$

4   Least upper bounds

After working through this section, you should be able to:

(a) explain the terms *bounded above*, *bounded below* and *bounded*;

(b) use the strategies for determining least upper bounds and greatest lower bounds;

(c) state the Least Upper Bound Property of $\mathbb{R}$ and the Greatest Lower Bound Property of $\mathbb{R}$.

4.1 Upper bounds and lower bounds

Any finite set of real numbers has a greatest element (and a least element), but this property does not necessarily hold for infinite sets. For example, neither of the sets $\mathbb{N} = \{1, 2, 3, \ldots\}$ and $[0, 2)$ has a greatest element. However, the set $[0, 2)$ is *bounded above* by 2, since all points of $[0, 2)$ are less than or equal to 2.

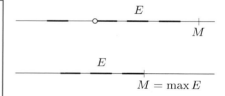

> **Definition**   A set $E \subseteq \mathbb{R}$ is **bounded above** if there is a real number M, called an **upper bound** of E, such that
>
> $$x \leq M, \quad \text{for all } x \in E.$$
>
> If the upper bound M belongs to E, then M is called the **maximum element** of E, denoted by $\max E$.

Geometrically, the set E is bounded above by M if no point of E lies to the right of M on the real line.

For example, if $E = [0, 2)$, then the numbers 2, 3, 3.5 and 157.1 are all upper bounds of E, whereas the numbers 1.995, 1.5, 0 and -157.1 are not upper bounds of E. Although it seems obvious that $[0, 2)$ has no maximum element, you may find it difficult to write down a proof. The following example shows you how to do this.

Example 4.1   Determine which of the following sets are bounded above and which have a maximum element.

(a) $E_1 = [0, 2)$

(b) $E_2 = \{1/n : n = 1, 2, \ldots\}$

(c) $E_3 = \mathbb{N}$

Solution

(a) The set E_1 is bounded above. For example, $M = 2$ is an upper bound of E_1, since

$$x \leq 2, \quad \text{for all } x \in E_1.$$

However, E_1 has no maximum element. For each x in E_1, we have $x < 2$, so there is a real number y such that

$$x < y < 2,$$

by the Density Property of $\mathbb{R}$. Hence $y \in E_1$, so x is not a maximum element of E_1.

The number 2 is not a maximum element, since $2 \notin E_1$.

(b) The set E_2 is bounded above. For example, $M = 1$ is an upper bound of E_2, since

$$\frac{1}{n} \leq 1, \quad \text{for } n = 1, 2, \ldots.$$

Also, since $1 \in E_2$ (take $n = 1$), we have

$$\max E_2 = 1.$$

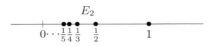

(c) The set E_3 is not bounded above. For each real number M, there is a positive integer n such that $n > M$, by the Archimedean Property of $\mathbb{R}$. Hence M is not an upper bound of E_3.

Since E_3 is not bounded above, it has no maximum element. ∎

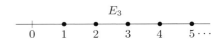

Exercise 4.1   Sketch the following sets, and determine which are bounded above and which have a maximum element.

(a) $E_1 = (-\infty, 1]$

(b) $E_2 = \{1 - 1/n : n = 1, 2, \ldots\}$

(c) $E_3 = \{n^2 : n = 1, 2, \ldots\}$

Similarly, we define *lower* bounds. For example, the interval $(0, 2)$ is bounded below by 0, since

$$0 \leq x, \quad \text{for all } x \in (0, 2).$$

However, 0 does not belong to $(0, 2)$, so 0 is not a minimum element of $(0, 2)$. In fact, $(0, 2)$ has no minimum element.

Definition   A set $E \subseteq \mathbb{R}$ is **bounded below** if there is a real number m, called a **lower bound** of E, such that

$$m \leq x, \quad \text{for all } x \in E.$$

If the lower bound m belongs to E, then m is called the **minimum element** of E, denoted by $\min E$.

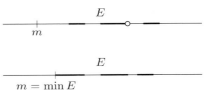

Geometrically, the set E is bounded below by m if no point of E lies to the left of m on the real line.

Exercise 4.2   Determine which of the following sets are bounded below and which have a minimum element.

(a) $E_1 = (-\infty, 1]$

(b) $E_2 = \{1 - 1/n : n = 1, 2, \ldots\}$

(c) $E_3 = \{n^2 : n = 1, 2, \ldots\}$

The following terminology is also useful.

Definition   A set $E \subseteq \mathbb{R}$ is **bounded** if E is bounded above and bounded below; the set E is **unbounded** if it is not bounded.

For example, in Exercise 4.2, the set $E_2 = \{1 - 1/n : n = 1, 2, \ldots\}$ is bounded, but $E_1 = (-\infty, 1]$ and $E_3 = \{n^2 : n = 1, 2, \ldots\}$ are unbounded.

4.2 Least upper and greatest lower bounds

We have seen that the set $[0, 2)$ has no maximum element. However, $[0, 2)$ has many upper bounds, for example, $2, 3, 3.5$ and 157.1. Among all these upper bounds, the number 2 is the *least* upper bound because any number less than 2 is not an upper bound of $[0, 2)$.

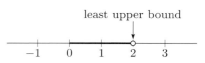

Definition A real number M is the **least upper bound**, or **supremum**, of a set $E \subseteq \mathbb{R}$ if

1. M is an upper bound of E;

2.   each $M' < M$ is not an upper bound of E.

In this case, we write $M = \sup E$.

The word supremum comes from the Latin word *supremus* meaning 'highest'.

If E has a maximum element $\max E$, then $\sup E = \max E$. For example, the closed interval $[0, 2]$ has maximum element 2, so it has least upper bound 2. We can think of the least upper bound of a set, when it exists, as a 'generalised maximum element'.

If a set does not have a maximum element, but is bounded above, then we may be able to guess the value of its least upper bound. As in the example $E = [0, 2)$, there may be an obvious 'missing point' at the upper end of the set. The next example shows you how to *prove* that your guess is correct.

Example 4.2   Prove that the least upper bound of $[0, 2)$ is 2.

Solution   We know that $M = 2$ is an upper bound of $[0, 2)$ because

$$x \leq 2, \quad \text{for all } x \in [0, 2).$$

If you are asked to 'prove' or 'determine' something, then you are expected to justify your answer.

To show that 2 is the *least* upper bound, we must prove that each number $M' < 2$ is *not* an upper bound of $[0, 2)$.

Suppose that $M' < 2$. We must find an element x in $[0, 2)$ which is greater than M'. But, by the Density Property, there is a real number x that is less than 2 and greater than both M' and 0. Thus $x \in [0, 2)$ and $x > M'$, which shows that M' is not an upper bound of $[0, 2)$. Hence $M = 2$ is the least upper bound of $[0, 2)$. ∎

The solution to Example 4.2 illustrates the strategy for determining the least upper bound of a set, if there is one.

Strategy 4.1   Given a subset E of $\mathbb{R}$, to show that M is the least upper bound, or supremum, of E, check that:

1. $x \leq M$, for *all* $x \in E$;

2.   if $M' < M$, then there is *some* $x \in E$ such that $x > M'$.

GUESS the value of M, then CHECK parts 1 and 2.

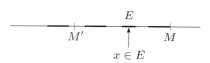

If M is an upper bound of a set E and $M \in E$, then parts 1 and 2 are automatically satisfied, so $M = \sup E = \max E$.

Example 4.3   Determine the least upper bound of

$$E = \{1 - 1/n^2 : n = 1, 2, \dots\}.$$

Solution   We guess from the diagram that the least upper bound of E is $M = 1$. Certainly, 1 is an upper bound of E, since

$$1 - \frac{1}{n^2} \leq 1, \quad \text{for } n = 1, 2, \dots.$$

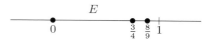

To check part 2 of Strategy 4.1, we need to show that if $M' < 1$, then there is some natural number n such that

$$1 - \frac{1}{n^2} > M'. \tag{4.1}$$

Suppose that $M' < 1$. We have

$$1 - \frac{1}{n^2} > M' \iff 1 - M' > \frac{1}{n^2}$$

$$\iff \frac{1}{1 - M'} < n^2 \quad \text{(since } 1 - M' > 0\text{)}$$

$$\iff \sqrt{\frac{1}{1 - M'}} < n \quad \text{(since } 1/(1 - M') > 0 \text{ and } n > 0\text{)}.$$

Here we rearrange inequality (4.1) into an equivalent form with just n on one side.

We can certainly choose n so that this final inequality holds, by the Archimedean Property of $\mathbb{R}$. Thus inequality (4.1) holds with this n.

Hence, by Strategy 4.1, the least upper bound of E is 1. ■

Remark Although we used double-headed arrows in this solution, the proof requires only the implications going from right to left. In other words, the proof uses only the fact that

$$1 - \frac{1}{n^2} > M' \impliedby \sqrt{\frac{1}{1 - M'}} < n.$$

— least upper bound.

Exercise 4.3 Determine $\sup E$, if it exists, for each of the following sets.

(a) $E_1 = (-\infty, 1]$

(b) $E_2 = \{1 - 1/n : n = 1, 2, \ldots\}$

(c) $E_3 = \{n^2 : n = 1, 2, \ldots\}$

Similarly, we define the notion of a *greatest lower bound*.

Definition A real number m is the **greatest lower bound**, or **infimum**, of a set $E \subseteq \mathbb{R}$ if

1. m is a lower bound of E;

2. each $m' > m$ is not a lower bound of E.

In this case, we write $m = \inf E$.

The word infimum comes from the Latin word *infimus* meaning 'least'.

If E has a minimum element, then $\inf E = \min E$. For example, the closed interval $[0, 2]$ has minimum element 0, so it has greatest lower bound 0.

The strategy for proving that a number is the greatest lower bound of a set is similar to Strategy 4.1.

Strategy 4.2 Given a subset E of $\mathbb{R}$, to show that m is the greatest lower bound, or infimum, of E, check that:

1. $x \geq m$, for *all* $x \in E$;

2. if $m' > m$, then there is *some* $x \in E$ such that $x < m'$.

GUESS the value of m, then CHECK parts 1 and 2.

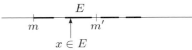

If m is a lower bound of E and $m \in E$, then parts 1 and 2 are automatically satisfied, so $m = \inf E = \min E$.

Exercise 4.4   Determine inf E, if it exists, for each of the following sets.

(a) $E_1 = (1, 5]$ (b) $E_2 = \{1/n^2 : n = 1, 2, \ldots\}$

4.3 Least Upper Bound Property

In the examples just given, it was straightforward to guess the values of $\sup E$ and $\inf E$. Sometimes, however, this is not the case. For example, if

$$E = \{(1 + 1/n)^n : n = 1, 2, \ldots\} = \{(\tfrac{2}{1})^1, (\tfrac{3}{2})^2, (\tfrac{4}{3})^3, \ldots\},$$

then it can be shown that E is bounded above by 3, but it is not so easy to guess the least upper bound of E.

This set E is discussed in the video for Unit AA2. It turns out that

$$\sup E = e = 2.718\,28\ldots.$$

In such cases, it is reassuring to know that $\sup E$ does exist, even though it may be difficult to find. This existence is guaranteed by the following fundamental result, on which many other results in analysis are based.

Least Upper Bound Property of $\mathbb{R}$ Let E be a non-empty subset of $\mathbb{R}$. If E is bounded above, then E has a least upper bound.

The Least Upper Bound Property of $\mathbb{R}$ is an example of an *existence theorem*, one which asserts that a mathematical object, such as a real number, exists with a certain property.

The Least Upper Bound Property of $\mathbb{R}$ is very plausible geometrically. If the set E lies entirely to the left of some number M, then you can imagine decreasing the value of M steadily until any further decrease causes M to be less than some point of E. At this point, $\sup E$ has been reached.

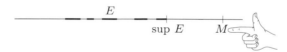

The Least Upper Bound Property of $\mathbb{R}$ can be used to show that $\mathbb{R}$ includes decimals which represent irrational numbers such as $\sqrt{2}$, as claimed earlier, and also to define arithmetic operations with decimals.

See Subsection 5.2.

There is a corresponding property for lower bounds.

Greatest Lower Bound Property of $\mathbb{R}$ Let E be a non-empty subset of $\mathbb{R}$. If E is bounded below, then E has a greatest lower bound.

Finally we prove the Least Upper Bound Property in the case when the set E contains at least one positive number. The proof in the general case can be reduced to this special case; we omit the details.

Proof   We know that E is bounded above and contains at least one positive number. We can now apply the following procedure to give us the successive digits in a decimal $a_0.a_1 a_2 \ldots$, which we then prove to be the least upper bound of E.

If you are short of time, omit this proof. It is included for the sake of completeness.

We choose in succession:

the greatest integer a_0 such that a_0 is not an upper bound of E;

the greatest digit a_1 such that $a_0.a_1$ is not an upper bound of E;

the greatest digit a_2 such that $a_0.a_1 a_2$ is not an upper bound of E;

$\vdots$

the greatest digit a_n such that $a_0.a_1 \ldots a_n$ is not an upper bound of E;

$\vdots$

Thus at the nth stage we choose the digit a_n so that

$$a_0.a_1a_2\ldots a_n \text{ is not an upper bound of } E; \tag{4.2}$$

$$a_0.a_1a_2\ldots a_n + \frac{1}{10^n} \text{ is an upper bound of } E. \tag{4.3}$$

We now use Strategy 4.1 to prove that the least upper bound of E is

$$a = a_0.a_1a_2\ldots.$$

First we have to show that a is an upper bound of E; that is, if $x \in E$, then $x \le a$. To do this, we prove the contrapositive statement: if $x > a$, then $x \notin E$. Let $x > a$ and represent x as a non-terminating decimal $x = x_0.x_1x_2\ldots$. Since $x > a$, there is an integer n such that

For example, if $x = 3.2$, then we write $x = 3.1999\ldots$.

$$a < x_0.x_1x_2\ldots x_n.$$

Hence

$$x_0.x_1x_2\ldots x_n \ge a_0.a_1a_2\ldots a_n + \frac{1}{10^n},$$

so $x_0.x_1x_2\ldots x_n$ is an upper bound of E, by statement (4.3). Since x is non-terminating, $x > x_0.x_1x_2\ldots x_n$, so $x \notin E$, as required.

Next we have to show that if $x < a$, then x is not an upper bound of E. Let $x < a$. Then there is an integer n such that

$$x < a_0.a_1a_2\ldots a_n,$$

so x is not an upper bound of E, by statement (4.2).

Thus we have proved that a is the least upper bound of E. ■

Further exercise

Exercise 4.5   In this exercise, take

$$E_1 = \{x \in \mathbb{Q} : 0 \le x < 1\} \quad \text{and} \quad E_2 = \{(1 + 1/n)^2 : n = 1, 2, \ldots\}.$$

(a) Prove that each of the sets E_1 and E_2 is bounded above. Which of them has a maximum element?

(b) Prove that each of the sets E_1 and E_2 is bounded below. Which of them has a minimum element?

(c) Determine the least upper bound of each of the sets E_1 and E_2.

(d) Determine the greatest lower bound of each of the sets E_1 and E_2.

5   Manipulating real numbers

After working through this section, you should be able to:

(a) explain how the Least Upper Bound Property is used to define arithmetical operations with real numbers;

(b) explain the meaning of rational powers.

This section is intended for reading only. There are no exercises on this section.

5.1 Arithmetic with real numbers

At the end of Section 1, we discussed the decimals

$$\sqrt{2} = 1.414\,213\,56\ldots \quad \text{and} \quad \pi = 3.141\,592\,65\ldots,$$

Here we are assuming that $\sqrt{2}$ and π can be represented as decimals.

and asked whether it is possible to add and multiply these numbers to obtain another real number. We now explain how this can be done using the Least Upper Bound Property of $\mathbb{R}$.

A natural way to obtain a sequence of approximations to the sum $\sqrt{2} + \pi$ is to truncate each of the above decimals and then form the sums of these truncations. If each of the decimals is truncated at the same decimal place, then we obtain sequences of approximations, which are increasing.

$\sqrt{2}$	π	$\sqrt{2} + \pi$
1	3	4
1.4	3.1	4.5
1.41	3.14	4.55
1.414	3.141	4.555
1.4142	3.1415	4.5557
$\vdots$	$\vdots$	$\vdots$

Intuitively we expect that the sum $\sqrt{2} + \pi$ is greater than each of the numbers in the right-hand column, but 'only just'. To accord with our intuition, therefore, we *define* the sum $\sqrt{2} + \pi$ to be the least upper bound of the set of numbers in the right-hand column; that is,

$$\sqrt{2} + \pi = \sup\{4, 4.5, 4.55, 4.555, 4.5557, \ldots\}.$$

To be sure that this definition makes sense, we need to show that this set is bounded above. But all the truncations of $\sqrt{2}$ are less than 1.5 and all those of π are less than 4. Hence, all the sums in the right-hand column are less than $1.5 + 4 = 5.5$. So, by the Least Upper Bound Property of $\mathbb{R}$, the set of numbers in the right-hand column *does* have a least upper bound and we *can* define $\sqrt{2} + \pi$ this way.

This method can be used to define the sum of any pair of positive real numbers.

Let us check that this method of adding decimals gives the correct answer when we use it in a familiar case. Consider the simple calculation

$$\tfrac{1}{3} + \tfrac{2}{3} = 0.333\ldots + 0.666\ldots.$$

This is not a practical method for adding rationals!

Truncating each of these decimals and forming the sums, we obtain the set

$$\{0, 0.9, 0.99, 0.999, \ldots\}.$$

The supremum of this set is $0.999\ldots = 1$, which is the correct answer.

Similarly, we can define the product of any two positive real numbers. For example, to define $\sqrt{2} \times \pi$, we can form the sequence of products of their truncations.

$\sqrt{2}$	π	$\sqrt{2} \times \pi$
1	3	3
1.4	3.1	4.34
1.41	3.14	4.4274
1.414	3.141	4.441374
1.4142	3.1415	4.4427093
$\vdots$	$\vdots$	$\vdots$

As before, we define $\sqrt{2} \times \pi$ to be the least upper bound of the set of numbers in the right-hand column.

Similar ideas can be used to define the operations of subtraction and division, but we omit the details.

In this way we can define arithmetic with real numbers in terms of the familiar arithmetic with rationals by using the Least Upper Bound Property of $\mathbb{R}$. Moreover, it can be proved that these operations in $\mathbb{R}$ satisfy all the usual properties of a field.

The properties of a field are listed in Subsection 1.5.

5.2 Existence of roots

Just as we usually take for granted the basic arithmetical operations with real numbers, so we usually assume that, given any positive real number a, there is a unique positive real number $b = \sqrt{a}$ such that $b^2 = a$. We now discuss the justification for this assumption.

First, here is a geometric justification. Given line segments of lengths 1 and a, we can construct a semicircle with diameter $a + 1$ as shown.

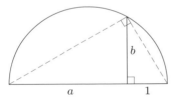

Using similar triangles, we find that

$$\frac{a}{b} = \frac{b}{1}, \quad \text{so} \quad b^2 = a.$$

This shows that there should be a positive real number b such that $b^2 = a$, in order that the length of the vertical line segment in this figure can be described exactly. But does $b = \sqrt{a}$ always exist *exactly* as a real number? In fact it does, and a more general result is true.

> **Theorem 5.1**   For each positive real number a and each integer $n > 1$, there is a unique positive real number b such that
> $$b^n = a.$$

A proof of this theorem is given in Unit AA4, Section 4.

We call this positive number b the **nth root** of a, and write $b = \sqrt[n]{a}$. We also define $\sqrt[n]{0} = 0$, since $0^n = 0$.

In the special case $a = 2$ and $n = 2$, Theorem 5.1 asserts the existence of a positive real number b such that

$$b^2 = 2.$$

Here is a direct proof of Theorem 5.1 in this special case. We choose the numbers $1, 1.4, 1.41, 1.414, \ldots$ to satisfy the inequalities:

$$\begin{aligned}
1^2 &< 2 < 2^2 \\
(1.4)^2 &< 2 < (1.5)^2 \\
(1.41)^2 &< 2 < (1.42)^2 \\
(1.414)^2 &< 2 < (1.415)^2 \\
&\;\;\vdots
\end{aligned} \qquad (5.1)$$

This process gives an infinite decimal $b = 1.414\ldots$ and we claim that

$$b^2 = (1.414\ldots)^2 = 2.$$

This can be proved using our method of multiplying decimals.

b	b	b^2
1	1	1
1.4	1.4	1.96
1.41	1.41	1.9881
1.414	1.414	1.999396
$\vdots$	$\vdots$	$\vdots$

We have to prove that the least upper bound of the set E of numbers in the right-hand column is 2. In other words,

$$\sup E = \sup\{1, (1.4)^2, (1.41)^2, (1.414)^2, \ldots\} = 2.$$

To do this, we use Strategy 4.1.

First we check that $M = 2$ is an upper bound of E. This follows from the left-hand inequalities in (5.1).

Next we check that if $M' < 2$, then there is a number in E which is greater than M'. To prove this, we put

$$x_0 = 1, \quad x_1 = 1.4, \quad x_2 = 1.41, \quad x_3 = 1.414, \quad \ldots.$$

By the right-hand inequalities in (5.1) we have, for $n = 0, 1, 2, \ldots$,

$$2 < \left(x_n + \frac{1}{10^n}\right)^2 = x_n^2 + \frac{2x_n}{10^n} + \left(\frac{1}{10^n}\right)^2,$$

so

$$x_n^2 > 2 - \frac{1}{10^n}\left(2x_n + \frac{1}{10^n}\right)$$

$$> 2 - \frac{5}{10^n} = 1.\underbrace{99\ldots95}_{n\text{ digits}}.$$

For example, in the case $n = 1$,

$$2 < \left(1.4 + \frac{1}{10}\right)^2 = (1.5)^2.$$

For example, in the case $n = 2$,

$$(1.41)^2 > 1.95.$$

Thus, if $M' < 2$, then we *can* choose n so large that $x_n^2 > M'$. This proves that the least upper bound of the set E is 2, so

$$b^2 = (1.414\ldots)^2 = 2,$$

as claimed. Thus $b = 1.414\ldots$ is a decimal representation of $\sqrt{2}$.

5.3 Powers

Having discussed nth roots, we are now in a position to define the expression a^x, where a is positive and x is a rational power (or exponent).

> **Definition**   If $a > 0$, $m \in \mathbb{Z}$ and $n \in \mathbb{N}$, then
> $$a^{m/n} = (\sqrt[n]{a})^m.$$

An equivalent definition is
$$a^{m/n} = \sqrt[n]{a^m}.$$

For example, for $a > 0$ with $m = 1$ we have $a^{1/n} = \sqrt[n]{a}$, and with $m = 2$ and $n = 3$ we have $a^{2/3} = (\sqrt[3]{a})^2$.

This notation is particularly useful because rational powers satisfy the following laws, whose proofs depend on Theorem 5.1.

> **Exponent Laws**   If $a, b > 0$ and $x, y \in \mathbb{Q}$, then
> $$a^x b^x = (ab)^x, \quad a^x a^y = a^{x+y} \quad \text{and} \quad (a^x)^y = a^{xy}.$$

For example:
$$2^{1/2} \times 3^{1/2} = 6^{1/2};$$
$$2^{1/2} \times 2^{1/3} = 2^{5/6};$$
$$(2^{1/2})^{1/3} = 2^{1/6}.$$

Remarks

1. If x and y are *integers*, then these laws also hold for all non-zero real numbers a and b, not just positive ones. However, if x and y are not integers, then we must have $a > 0$ and $b > 0$.

For example, $(-1)^{1/2}$ is not defined as a real number.

2. Each positive number has *two* nth roots when n is even. For example, $2^2 = (-2)^2 = 4$. We adopt the convention that, for $a > 0$, $\sqrt[n]{a}$ and $a^{1/n}$ always denote the *positive* nth root of a. If we wish to refer to both roots (for example, when solving equations), then we write $\pm \sqrt[n]{a}$.

We conclude this section by briefly discussing the meaning of a^x when $a > 0$ and x is an arbitrary real number. We have defined a^x when x is rational, but the same definition does not work if x is irrational. However, it is common practice to write expressions such as

$$\sqrt{2}^{\sqrt{2}}$$

and even to apply the Exponent Laws to give equalities such as

$$\left(\sqrt{2}^{\sqrt{2}}\right)^{\sqrt{2}} = \sqrt{2}^{\sqrt{2} \times \sqrt{2}} = (\sqrt{2})^2 = 2.$$

Such manipulations *can* be justified, and by the end of Analysis Block A you will have seen one way to do this. Moreover, the justification uses several key ideas from the block, including convergence of sequences, convergence of series and continuity.

See Unit AA4, Section 4.

Solutions to the exercises

1.1 Since $45 \times 20 = 900$ and $17 \times 53 = 901$, we have $45/53 < 17/20$. Thus

$$-1 < -\frac{17}{20} < -\frac{45}{53} < 0 < \frac{45}{53} < \frac{17}{20} < 1.$$

1.2 Let a, b be distinct rationals, where $a < b$. Let $c = \frac{1}{2}(a + b)$; then c is rational, and

$$c - a = \tfrac{1}{2}(b - a) > 0,$$
$$b - c = \tfrac{1}{2}(b - a) > 0,$$

so $a < c < b$.

1.3 We have $\frac{1}{7} = 0.142\,857\,142\,857\ldots$.

1.4 **(a)** Let $x = 0.\overline{231}$.
Multiplying both sides by 10^3, we obtain

$$1000x = 231.\overline{231} = 231 + x.$$

Hence

$$999x = 231, \quad \text{so} \quad x = \frac{231}{999} = \frac{77}{333}.$$

(b) Let $x = 0.\overline{81}$.
Multiplying both sides by 10^2, we obtain

$$100x = 81.\overline{81} = 81 + x.$$

Hence

$$99x = 81, \quad \text{so} \quad x = \frac{81}{99} = \frac{9}{11}.$$

Thus

$$2.2\overline{81} = 2 + \frac{2}{10} + \frac{9}{110} = \frac{251}{110}.$$

1.5 $\dfrac{17}{20} = 0.85$ and $\dfrac{45}{53} = 0.84\ldots$, so $\dfrac{45}{53} < \dfrac{17}{20}$.

1.6 **(a)** For example,

$$x = 0.34 \quad \text{and} \quad y = 0.340\,010\,010\,001\ldots.$$

(b) Here is one method. Let

$$a = a_0.a_1a_2\ldots \quad \text{and} \quad b = b_0.b_1b_2\ldots,$$

where $a_0, b_0 \geq 0$. We can arrange that a does not end in recurring 9s, whereas b does not terminate.
Since $a < b$, there is an integer n such that

$$a_0 = b_0, \, a_1 = b_1, \, \ldots, \, a_{n-1} = b_{n-1}, \text{ but } a_n < b_n.$$

Thus $x = a_0.a_1 \ldots a_{n-1}b_n$ is rational and

$$a < x < b.$$

Since $x < b$ and b does not terminate, we can attach a non-recurring tail to x to obtain an irrational y such that

$$a < x < y < b.$$

1.7 **(a)** Putting all the fractions over the common denominator of 180, we obtain

$$\frac{3}{20} < \frac{7}{45} < \frac{1}{6} < \frac{11}{60} < \frac{7}{36}.$$

(Alternatively, we can compare the decimal representations of these fractions.)

(b) $0.\overline{465} < 0.4655 < 0.46\overline{5} < 0.4656 < 0.4\overline{65}$

1.8 **(a)** If $x = 0.\overline{481}$, then

$$1000x = 481.\overline{481} = 481 + x.$$

Hence $x = 481/999 = 13/27$.

(b) If $y = 0.\overline{1}$, then $10y = 1.1 = 1 + y$, so $y = 1/9$. Hence

$$0.48\overline{1} = \frac{48}{100} + \frac{1}{900} = \frac{433}{900}.$$

1.9 $x + y = \dfrac{21}{99} + \dfrac{2}{9} = \dfrac{43}{99} = 0.\overline{43}$

$$xy = \frac{21}{99} \times \frac{2}{9} = \frac{14}{297} = 0.\overline{047\,138}$$

1.10 For example, $x = 0.1195$ and $y = 0.119\,501\,001\ldots$.

2.1 **(a)** Rule 2 gives $x + 3 > 5$.

(b) Rules 1 and 3 give $2 - x < 0$.

(c) Rules 2 and 3 give $5x + 2 > 12$.

(d) Part (c) and Rule 4 give $1/(5x + 2) < 1/12$.

2.2 **(a)** Rearranging the inequality using Rule 1 and Rule 3 (with $c = -4$), we obtain

$$\frac{4x - x^2 - 7}{x^2 - 1} \geq 3 \iff \frac{4x - x^2 - 7}{x^2 - 1} - 3 \geq 0$$
$$\iff \frac{4x - 4x^2 - 4}{x^2 - 1} \geq 0$$
$$\iff \frac{x^2 - x + 1}{x^2 - 1} \leq 0$$
$$\iff \frac{\left(x - \frac{1}{2}\right)^2 + \frac{3}{4}}{x^2 - 1} \leq 0.$$

Since $(x - \frac{1}{2})^2 + \frac{3}{4} > 0$, for all x, the inequality holds if and only if $x^2 - 1 = (x - 1)(x + 1) < 0$.
Hence the solution set is

$$\left\{ x : \frac{4x - x^2 - 7}{x^2 - 1} \geq 3 \right\} = (-1, 1).$$

(b) Rearranging the inequality, we obtain

$$2x^2 \geq (x + 1)^2 \iff 2x^2 \geq x^2 + 2x + 1$$
$$\iff x^2 - 2x - 1 \geq 0 \quad \text{(Rule 2)}$$
$$\iff (x - 1)^2 \geq 2.$$

Hence the solution set is

$$\{x : 2x^2 \geq (x+1)^2\}$$
$$= \{x : x - 1 \leq -\sqrt{2}\} \cup \{x : x - 1 \geq \sqrt{2}\}$$
$$= (-\infty, 1 - \sqrt{2}] \cup [1 + \sqrt{2}, \infty).$$

2.3 We can obtain an equivalent inequality by squaring, provided that both sides are non-negative. Now $\sqrt{2x^2 - 2}$ is defined, and non-negative, when $2x^2 - 2 \geq 0$, that is, for $x^2 \geq 1$. Thus $\sqrt{2x^2 - 2}$ is defined if x lies in $(-\infty, -1] \cup [1, \infty)$.

For $x \geq 1$,

$$\sqrt{2x^2 - 2} > x \iff 2x^2 - 2 > x^2 \quad \text{(Rule 5, } p = 2)$$
$$\iff x^2 > 2.$$

So the part of the solution set in $[1, \infty)$ is $(\sqrt{2}, \infty)$.

For $x \leq -1$,

$$\sqrt{2x^2 - 2} \geq 0 > x,$$

so the whole of $(-\infty, -1]$ lies in the solution set. Hence the complete solution set is

$$\{x : \sqrt{2x^2 - 2} > x\} = (-\infty, -1] \cup (\sqrt{2}, \infty).$$

2.4 (a) We have

$$|2x^2 - 13| < 5 \iff -5 < 2x^2 - 13 < 5 \quad \text{(Rule 6)}$$
$$\iff 8 < 2x^2 < 18$$
$$\iff 4 < x^2 < 9$$
$$\iff 2 < |x| < 3 \quad \text{(Rule 5, } p = 2).$$

Hence the solution set is

$$\{x : |2x^2 - 13| < 5\} = (-3, -2) \cup (2, 3).$$

(b) We have

$$|x - 1| \leq 2|x + 1| \iff (x-1)^2 \leq 4(x+1)^2$$
$$\iff x^2 - 2x + 1 \leq 4x^2 + 8x + 4$$
$$\iff 0 \leq 3x^2 + 10x + 3$$
$$\iff 0 \leq (3x + 1)(x + 3).$$

Hence the solution set is

$$\{x : |x - 1| \leq 2|x + 1|\} = (-\infty, -3] \cup [-\tfrac{1}{3}, \infty).$$

2.5 (a) We have

$$\frac{x-1}{x^2+4} < \frac{x+1}{x^2-4} \iff 0 < \frac{x+1}{x^2-4} - \frac{x-1}{x^2+4}$$
$$\iff 0 < \frac{2x(x+4)}{(x-2)(x+2)(x^2+4)}.$$

Using a sign table including the factors $x, x + 4, x - 2$ and $x + 2$, we find that the solution set is

$$\left\{ x : \frac{x-1}{x^2+4} < \frac{x+1}{x^2-4} \right\} \quad \text{crit values } 0, -4, 2, -2$$
$$= (-\infty, -4) \cup (-2, 0) \cup (2, \infty).$$

(b) The expression $\sqrt{4x - 3}$ is defined, and non-negative, for $x \geq \tfrac{3}{4}$.

For $x \geq \tfrac{3}{4}$,

$$\sqrt{4x - 3} > x \iff 4x - 3 > x^2$$
$$\iff 0 > x^2 - 4x + 3$$
$$\iff 0 > (x - 1)(x - 3).$$

Hence the solution set is

$$\{x : \sqrt{4x - 3} > x\} = (1, 3).$$

(c) $|17 - 2x^4| \leq 15 \iff -15 \leq 17 - 2x^4 \leq 15$
$$\iff -32 \leq -2x^4 \leq -2$$
$$\iff 16 \geq x^4 \geq 1$$
$$\iff 2 \geq |x| \geq 1$$

Hence the solution set is

$$\{x : |17 - 2x^4| \leq 15\} = [-2, -1] \cup [1, 2].$$

3.1 (a) Suppose that $|a| \leq \tfrac{1}{2}$.

The Triangle Inequality gives

$$|a + 1| \leq |a| + 1$$
$$\leq \tfrac{1}{2} + 1 \quad \left(\text{since } |a| \leq \tfrac{1}{2}\right)$$
$$= \tfrac{3}{2}.$$

Hence

$$|a| \leq \tfrac{1}{2} \implies |a + 1| \leq \tfrac{3}{2}.$$

(b) Suppose that $|b| < \tfrac{1}{2}$.

The backwards form of the Triangle Inequality gives

$$|b^3 - 1| \geq \big||b^3| - 1\big|$$
$$= \big||b|^3 - 1\big|$$
$$\geq 1 - |b|^3.$$

Now

$$|b| < \tfrac{1}{2} \implies |b|^3 < \tfrac{1}{8} \implies 1 - |b|^3 > \tfrac{7}{8},$$

so, from the previous chain of inequalities,

$$|b| < \tfrac{1}{2} \implies |b^3 - 1| > \tfrac{7}{8}.$$

3.2 Rearranging the inequality, we obtain

$$\frac{3n}{n^2 + 2} < 1 \iff 3n < n^2 + 2 \quad \text{(since } n^2 + 2 > 0)$$
$$\iff 0 < n^2 - 3n + 2$$
$$\iff 0 < (n - 1)(n - 2).$$

This final inequality certainly holds for $n > 2$, so

$$\frac{3n}{n^2 + 2} < 1, \quad \text{for } n > 2.$$

3.3 Applying the Binomial Theorem in the form

$$(1+x)^n = 1 + nx + \frac{n(n-1)}{2!}x^2 + \cdots + x^n,$$

with $x = 1/n$, we obtain, for $n \geq 2$,

$$\left(1 + \frac{1}{n}\right)^n = 1 + n\left(\frac{1}{n}\right) + \frac{n(n-1)}{2!}\left(\frac{1}{n}\right)^2 + \cdots$$

$$\geq 1 + 1 + \frac{1}{2}\left(1 - \frac{1}{n}\right)$$

$$= \frac{5}{2} - \frac{1}{2n}.$$

Since this inequality also holds for $n = 1$, we deduce that

$$\left(1 + \frac{1}{n}\right)^n \geq \frac{5}{2} - \frac{1}{2n}, \quad \text{for } n \geq 1.$$

3.4 (a) Using Rule 3 for rearranging inequalities, we obtain

$$2n^3 \geq (n+1)^3 \Leftrightarrow 2 \geq \left(\frac{n+1}{n}\right)^3.$$

The inequality on the right is certainly true for $n = 4$, since $(5/4)^3 = 125/64 < 2$. Also,

$$\left(\frac{n+1}{n}\right)^3 = \left(1 + \frac{1}{n}\right)^3 \leq \left(1 + \frac{1}{4}\right)^3, \quad \text{for } n \geq 4,$$

so

$$\left(\frac{n+1}{n}\right)^3 \leq 2, \quad \text{for } n \geq 4.$$

Hence

$$2n^3 \geq (n+1)^3, \quad \text{for } n \geq 4.$$

(b) Here we use mathematical induction. Let $P(n)$ be the statement

$$2^n \geq n^3.$$

Step 1: $P(10)$ is true because $2^{10} = 1024 > 10^3$.

Step 2: We show that

$$P(k) \text{ true} \Rightarrow P(k+1) \text{ true}, \quad \text{for } k \geq 10;$$

that is

$$2^k \geq k^3 \Rightarrow 2^{k+1} \geq (k+1)^3, \quad \text{for } k \geq 10.$$

Suppose that $2^k \geq k^3$ for some $k \geq 10$. Then

$$2^{k+1} = 2 \times 2^k \geq 2k^3.$$

Thus it is sufficient to prove that

$$2k^3 \geq (k+1)^3, \quad \text{for } k \geq 10.$$

By part (a), this inequality is true. (It holds for $k \geq 4$.) Hence

$$2^{k+1} \geq (k+1)^3.$$

Thus

$$P(k) \text{ true} \Rightarrow P(k+1) \text{ true}, \quad \text{for } k \geq 10.$$

Therefore, by mathematical induction,

$$2^n \geq n^3, \quad \text{for } n \geq 10.$$

3.5 Suppose that $a > 0$ and $a^2 > 2$. By the rules for rearranging inequalities into equivalent forms,

$$\frac{1}{2}\left(a + \frac{2}{a}\right) < a \Leftrightarrow \frac{a}{2} + \frac{1}{a} < a$$

$$\Leftrightarrow \frac{1}{a} < \frac{a}{2}$$

$$\Leftrightarrow 2 < a^2 \quad (\text{since } a > 0).$$

Since the final inequality is true, the first inequality must also be true. Hence

$$\frac{1}{2}\left(a + \frac{2}{a}\right) < a.$$

3.6 Suppose that $|a| \leq 1$. By the backwards form of the Triangle Inequality,

$$|a - 3| \geq ||a| - 3|$$

$$\geq 3 - |a|$$

$$\geq 2 \quad (\text{since } |a| \leq 1).$$

Hence

$$|a| \leq 1 \Rightarrow |a - 3| \geq 2.$$

3.7 We rearrange the inequality into a simpler equivalent form:

$$(a^2 + b^2)(c^2 + d^2) \geq (ac + bd)^2$$

$$\Leftrightarrow a^2c^2 + a^2d^2 + b^2c^2 + b^2d^2 \geq a^2c^2 + 2acbd + b^2d^2$$

$$\Leftrightarrow a^2d^2 + b^2c^2 - 2acbd \geq 0 \quad (\text{Rule 1})$$

$$\Leftrightarrow (ad - bc)^2 \geq 0.$$

The last equality is true for all $a, b, c, d \in \mathbb{R}$, so the first inequality must also be true, as required.

3.8 (a) By the Binomial Theorem for $n \geq 2$,

$$3^n = (1 + 2)^n \geq 1 + 2n + \frac{n(n-1)}{2!}2^2$$

$$= 1 + 2n + 2n(n-1)$$

$$= 1 + 2n^2.$$

Since the inequality is also true for $n = 1$, we obtain

$$3^n \geq 1 + 2n^2, \quad \text{for } n \geq 1.$$

(b) To use mathematical induction, we let $P(n)$ be the statement

$$3^n \geq 2n^2 + 1.$$

Step 1: We noted in part (a) that $P(1)$ is true.

Step 2: We now show that if $P(k)$ is true for some k, then $P(k+1)$ is also true; that is,

$$3^k \geq 2k^2 + 1 \Rightarrow 3^{k+1} \geq 2(k+1)^2 + 1, \quad \text{for } k \geq 1.$$

Suppose that $3^k \geq 2k^2 + 1$. Then

$$3^{k+1} = 3 \times 3^k \geq 3(2k^2 + 1).$$

Thus it is sufficient to prove that

$$3(2k^2 + 1) \geq 2(k+1)^2 + 1.$$

Now
$$3(2k^2 + 1) \geq 2(k+1)^2 + 1$$
$$\Leftrightarrow \ 6k^2 + 3 \geq 2k^2 + 4k + 3$$
$$\Leftrightarrow \ 4k^2 \geq 4k,$$
and this last equivalent inequality is certainly true for $k \geq 1$. Hence
$$3^{k+1} \geq 2(k+1)^2 + 1.$$
Thus we have shown that
$$P(k) \text{ true} \ \Rightarrow \ P(k+1) \text{ true}, \quad \text{for } k = 1, 2, \ldots.$$
Hence $P(n)$ is true, for $n = 1, 2, \ldots$, by mathematical induction.

3.9 Applying Bernoulli's Inequality with $x = 2/n$, we obtain
$$(1 + 2/n)^n \geq 1 + n(2/n) = 3.$$
Hence
$$1 + 2/n \geq 3^{1/n}, \quad \text{for } n = 1, 2, \ldots.$$
Applying Bernoulli's Inequality with $x = -2/(3n)$, we obtain
$$(1 - 2/(3n))^n \geq 1 + n(-2/(3n)) = 1/3.$$
Hence
$$\frac{3n-2}{3n} \geq \left(\frac{1}{3}\right)^{1/n}, \quad \text{for } n = 1, 2, \ldots,$$
so
$$3^{1/n} \geq \frac{3n}{3n-2} = 1 + \frac{2}{3n-2}, \quad \text{for } n = 1, 2, \ldots.$$

4.1 (a)

E_1

The set E_1 is bounded above. For example, $M = 1$ is an upper bound of E_1, since
$$x \leq 1, \quad \text{for all } x \in E_1.$$
Also, $\max E_1 = 1$, since $1 \in E_1$.

(b)

E_2

The set E_2 is bounded above. For example, $M = 1$ is an upper bound of E_2, since
$$1 - \frac{1}{n} \leq 1, \quad \text{for } n = 1, 2, \ldots.$$
However, E_2 has no maximum element. If $x \in E_2$, then $x = 1 - 1/n$, for some $n \in \mathbb{N}$, so there is another element of E_2, for example $1 - 1/(n+1)$, such that
$$1 - \frac{1}{n} < 1 - \frac{1}{n+1} \quad \left(\text{since } \frac{1}{n+1} < \frac{1}{n}\right).$$
Hence x is not a maximum element of E_2.

(c)

E_3

The set E_3 is not bounded above. For each real number M, there is a positive integer n such that $n^2 > M$ (for instance, take $n > M$, which implies that $n^2 \geq n > M$). Hence M is not an upper bound of E_3.

It follows that E_3 cannot have a maximum element.

4.2 (a) The set $E_1 = (-\infty, 1]$ is not bounded below. For each real number m, there is a negative real number x such that $x < m$. Since $x \in E_1$, the number m is not a lower bound of E_1.

It follows that E_1 cannot have a minimum element.

(b) The set E_2 is bounded below by 0, since
$$1 - \frac{1}{n} \geq 0, \quad \text{for } n = 1, 2, \ldots.$$
Also, $0 \in E_2$, so $\min E_2 = 0$.

(c) The set E_3 is bounded below by 1, since
$$n^2 \geq 1, \quad \text{for } n = 1, 2, \ldots.$$
Also, $1 \in E_3$, so $\min E_3 = 1$.

4.3 (a) The set $E_1 = (-\infty, 1]$ has maximum element 1, so
$$\sup E_1 = \max E_1 = 1.$$

(b) We use Strategy 4.1. We know that the set $E_2 = \{1 - 1/n : n = 1, 2, \ldots\}$ is bounded above by 1, since
$$1 - \frac{1}{n} \leq 1, \quad \text{for } n = 1, 2, \ldots.$$
To show that $M = 1$ is the least upper bound of E_2, we have to prove that if $M' < 1$, then there is an element $1 - 1/n$ of E_2 such that
$$1 - \frac{1}{n} > M'.$$
Suppose that $M' < 1$. We have
$$1 - \frac{1}{n} > M'$$
$$\Leftrightarrow \ 1 - M' > \frac{1}{n}$$
$$\Leftrightarrow \ 1/(1 - M') < n \quad (\text{since } 1 - M' > 0).$$
Thus if we take a positive integer n so large that $n > 1/(1 - M')$, then we obtain a number $1 - 1/n$ in E_2 such that $1 - 1/n > M'$, as required.

Hence 1 is the least upper bound of E_2.

(c) The set $E_3 = \{n^2 : n = 1, 2, \ldots\}$ is not bounded above, so it cannot have a least upper bound.

4.4 (a) We use Strategy 4.2. We know that the set $E_1 = (1, 5]$ is bounded below by 1, since

$$1 \leq x, \quad \text{for all } x \in E_1.$$

To show that $m = 1$ is the greatest lower bound of E_1, we prove that if $m' > 1$, then there is an element x in E_1 which is less than m'. But if $m' > 1$, then there is a real number x such that

$$1 < x < m' \quad \text{and} \quad 1 < x \leq 5,$$

so $x \in E_1$, as required.

Hence 1 is the greatest lower bound of E_1.

(b) We use Strategy 4.2. We know that the set $E_2 = \{1/n^2 : n = 1, 2, \ldots\}$ is bounded below by 0, since

$$0 < 1/n^2, \quad \text{for } n = 1, 2, \ldots.$$

To show that $m = 0$ is the greatest lower bound of E_2, we prove that if $m' > 0$, then there is an element $1/n^2$ in E_2 such that $1/n^2 < m'$.

But if $m' > 0$, then we have

$$\frac{1}{n^2} < m' \Leftrightarrow n^2 > \frac{1}{m'}$$
$$\Leftrightarrow n > \sqrt{1/m'}.$$

Thus if we take a positive integer n so large that $n > \sqrt{1/m'}$, then we obtain a number $1/n^2$ in E_2 such that $1/n^2 < m'$, as required.

Hence 0 is the greatest lower bound of E_2.

4.5 (a) The set E_1 is bounded above by 1, since

$$x \leq 1, \quad \text{for } x \in E_1.$$

But E_1 does not have a maximum element. For each $x \in E_1$ we have $0 \leq x < 1$, so there is a rational number y such that $x < y < 1$. Since $y \in E_1$, we deduce that x is not a maximum element of E_1.

The set E_2 is bounded above by 4, since

$$\left(1 + \frac{1}{n}\right)^2 \leq (1 + 1)^2 = 4, \quad \text{for } n = 1, 2, \ldots.$$

Also, E_2 does have a maximum element, namely 4 (take $n = 1$).

(b) The set E_1 is bounded below by 0, since

$$x \geq 0, \quad \text{for } x \in E_1.$$

Also, E_1 does have a minimum element, namely 0.

The set E_2 is bounded below by 1, since

$$\left(1 + \frac{1}{n}\right)^2 \geq 1, \quad \text{for } n = 1, 2, \ldots.$$

But E_2 does not have a minimum element. For each x in E_2, we have $x = (1 + 1/n)^2$, for some n, so

$$y = (1 + 1/(n+1))^2 < x \quad \text{and} \quad y \in E_2.$$

Hence x is not a minimum element of E_2.

(c) The least upper bound of E_1 is $M = 1$. As noted in part (a), 1 is an upper bound of E_1. To see that it is the *least* upper bound, suppose that $M' < 1$. Then there is a rational number x such that $M' < x < 1$. Since $x \in E_1$, we deduce that M' is not an upper bound of E_1. Hence the least upper bound of E_1 is 1.

The least upper bound of E_2 is 4, since $\max E_2 = 4$.

(d) The greatest lower bound of E_1 is 0, since $\min E_1 = 0$.

The greatest lower bound of E_2 is $m = 1$. As noted in part (b), 1 is a lower bound of E_2. To see that it is the *greatest* lower bound, suppose that $m' > 1$. We want to find an element $x = (1 + 1/n)^2$ of E_2 such that $x < m'$.

Since $\sqrt{m'} > 1$, we have

$$\left(1 + \frac{1}{n}\right)^2 < m' \Leftrightarrow 1 + \frac{1}{n} < \sqrt{m'}$$
$$\Leftrightarrow \frac{1}{n} < \sqrt{m'} - 1$$
$$\Leftrightarrow n > 1/(\sqrt{m'} - 1).$$

Choosing a positive integer n so large that $n > 1/(\sqrt{m'} - 1)$, we obtain $x = (1 + 1/n)^2 < m'$, as required. Hence m' is not a lower bound of E_2, so the greatest lower bound of E_2 is 1.

Index